A NOT-SO-PERFECT GUIDE TO WHO
YOU ARE AND WHY YOU'RE HERE

© 2016 Mike Foster/Slowboat Publishing

951-200-4123
www.SecondChance.org
Contact@SecondChance.org

Cover design and book layout: Ashton Owens/Wheelhouse
Exercise design and layout: Mike Foster
Additional design support: Josh Webb

Printed in the United States of America

FOR THOSE READY TO LIVE
EACH DAY IN THE WONDER
OF GOD'S GRACE

THIS BOOK BELONGS TO:

★ ★

_____

WRITE YOUR NAME HERE:

_____

WRITE YOUR NAME MESSY RIGHT HERE:

_____

WRITE YOUR NICKNAME HERE:

_____

WRITE YOUR NAME SUPER TINY ON THIS LINE:

★ ★ ★

IF SOMEONE FINDS YOUR BOOK,
DO YOU WANT THEM TO RETURN IT TO YOU?

◯ _YES!_   ◯ _NO, JUST KEEP IT!_

INSTRUCTIONS ON HOW TO RETURN MY BOOK:

_____

TODAY YOU ARE
YOU, THAT IS
TRUER THAN
TRUE. THERE
IS NO ONE ALIVE
WHO IS YOUER
THAN YOU.

-Dr. Seuss

LIFE IS NOT A

PROBLEM

TO BE SOLVED,

BUT A REALITY

TO BE

EXPERIENCED.

—

-Søren Kierkegaard

A NOTE FROM MIKE

Hi! My name is Mike Foster and I am the creator of *Wonderlife*.

As I designed this workbook, I tried to imagine what questions, struggles and hopes you might have right now. Maybe during this season you're brimming with dreams for your future, or perhaps you feel discouraged about how life is currently going.

Either way, I believe the four principles in this workbook can help you embrace all that God has for your story. I know that these basic concepts, based in Psalm 139, have personally helped me and the many individuals I have counseled over the past decade.

I have kept the content in *Wonderlife* simple and straightforward. I'm not one of those fancy, intellectual types, and I also have a lot to learn myself. That's why I call it a "not-so-perfect guide." I must also confess that this workbook won't fix all your problems and you might not agree with everything I say. But I believe that no matter what your life looks like right now, the story that God invites you into can be wonderful.

Cheering you on,

TABLE OF CONTENTS

YOU DIDN'T COME THIS FAR
TO ONLY COME THIS FAR.

WONDERLIFE IS BASED ON FOUR SIMPLE PRINCIPLES THAT WILL HELP YOU EMBRACE THE PURPOSE GOD HAS FOR YOUR LIFE.

THIS CREATIVE WORKBOOK IS DESIGNED TO SHOW YOU HOW TO EXPERIENCE THE JOY AND WONDER OF BEING THE YOU GOD MADE YOU TO BE.

HOW TO USE THIS BOOK

The *Wonderlife* workbook includes five strategic elements to help create an experience that leads to positive growth and connection. Every chapter contains these key learning elements:

1. MAIN READINGS

The main reading sections will help set up the big idea and unpack the key principles of that particular chapter and lifemark.

2. EXPLORE

The explore pages contain creative exercises to help capture your ideas, thoughts and beliefs. Think of this section like a strategic journal that will help you do some important self-reflection.

3. BREAKOUT NUGGETS

The breakout nuggets are extremely short readings that highlight a key idea. If you're not a big reader, these will be very helpful.

4. GROUP UP

This is where you meet with friends and discuss the topics of *Wonderlife*. I believe the real breakthrough times of *Wonderlife* will happen when we share our lives and stories together.

5. JUMP IN

On these pages I offer up some fun life experiments to try out during the week. These are simple next steps to help you put into action some of the *Wonderlife* concepts.

TIPS & SUGGESTIONS

Have a real desire to grow and learn.
Share honestly what you're learning. Conversations are key.
Make a mess inside. Write. Draw. Scribble. Color.
At times, you will want to quit. That's normal. But keep going.
Use the teaching videos at www.SecondChance.org/video.
There are no "right" answers for the exercises or questions.
Have fun. Enjoy the experience. Know that God is for you.

SHARE ONLINE

I believe your story, dreams and passions are something
that can help others grow and learn. As you engage in the
different exercises, quotes, readings and activities, take a
moment and inspire us with your life and learnings on your
social media platforms.

Use the hashtag:
#MYWONDERLIFE

GROUP LEADER TIPS

Thanks so much for being willing to host a *Wonderlife* group. Here are a few key tips that will definitely help you be a great host. I have also included a link on the next page to other group leader resources that might be helpful too.

1. Organize the group time and meeting place. Invite friends, neighbors and people that you know.

2. Make sure everyone has their own *Wonderlife* workbook. Due to the personal nature of the exercises, it's not recommended that people share a workbook.

3. Remind people that they need to do the reading and exercises for the first week before they attend the first group session. We will dive right in!

4. Create a comfortable, welcoming and relaxed atmosphere.

5. Your main job is to read the group questions and facilitate conversations. You don't need to teach, preach or have all the answers.

6. Snacks and drinks are always a good idea. Share this responsibility with other group members.

7. As the group leader, take on the responsibility of starting and ending on time. Respect people's time and schedules. This is very important.

8. Be familiar with the questions and activities. It's also a good idea to watch the group videos ahead of time at SecondChance.org/video.

rescue
A C A D E M Y

Rescue Academy is a seven-part online course that will transform you from advice-giver to life-giver. In this course I will teach you the skills and strategies to help you impact friends, family and those you influence. You will walk away overflowing with confidence and the know-how needed to facilitate life-changing conversations.

Learn more at:
SECONDCHANCE.ORG/RESCUE

THE GROUP VIDEOS

Hey, guys! I've created a ten-minute teaching video for each session of *Wonderlife*. In these short and snappy videos I share key insights about the topic and unpack some fresh content to set your group up for some terrific conversations. I believe these videos are an awesome way to enhance and maximize your experience, so I've created two options for you to access them.

VIDEO OPTION ONE:

Stream all the *Wonderlife* group discussion videos
for free and access bonus content by registering at:
SecondChance.org/video

VIDEO OPTION TWO:

Purchase the *Wonderlife* group discussion DVD at:
SecondChance.org/store

DON'T BE AFRAID, FOR I AM WITH YOU.
DON'T BE DISCOURAGED, FOR I AM YOUR GOD.
- Isaiah 41:10

INTRODUCTION

Let's start with the truest truth of the human experience. Life is hard and awesome and no one has it totally figured it out. Why? Because life is made up of opposites. It is both sweet and sour. It's crap and cupcakes. Good days and disasters. Author Glennon Doyle Melton describes our stories as both beautiful and brutal and refers to them as "brutiful." I think she is right.

Over the years I've learned that life doesn't play by my rules. I wish it did, but unfortunately it doesn't follow orders very well. Life is a wild child who loves plot twists, cliffhangers and tearjerkers. And the moment you foolishly believe you have it figured out, life suddenly jerks, spins and flips you upside down just for giggles. *Thanks, life. Thanks a lot!*

But in spite of this fact, here you are. Alive. Ready. Searching for something. Sure, you've taken some sucker punches to the gut, but you're still standing, right? You may be exhausted, discouraged and losing hope, but you're not quitting, are you? This might be your defining moment when you decide to either radically embrace life's beautiful wonder or curse its tragic unfairness.

I know sometimes our stories can feel so lost and incomplete. It's frustrating, isn't it? Often our life looks like a 5,000-piece puzzle set where 200 pieces have gone missing, 400 pieces won't fit anywhere and the rest of the puzzle parts are thrown all over the house. The hope of completing the picture is not looking so good, is it?

Perhaps you're starting to ask those two questions we all must wrestle with: "Who am I?" and "Why am I here?" And if we had a solid answer, then maybe all of life's craziness might make more sense.

Right now you and I live in a unique time when our generation has lost our most precious possession—ourselves. We live in a perpetual identity crisis. We are prone to habitually reinvent ourselves and let the latest trends define us.

Are we our titles? Are we our online tribes? Affiliations? Are we hipster or gangster? Are we our relationship status on Facebook or just a collection of society's toxic labels?

And the problem is that if we don't know who we are, how could we ever know what to do? Are you supposed to "fake it till you make it" or "work hard and play by the rules"? Should you "be all that you can be" or "work for a cause and not applause"? Are you supposed to "just do it" or "wish upon a star"? No one seems to know.

So who should we look to for these important answers? You've discovered by now that there are no shortage of advice givers ready to tell you who you are and what to do. Books, conferences and motivational infomercials all seek to sell you their formulas and magical potions to fix your meaningless life.

And then there are our parents, friends, teachers, coaches, gurus and well-meaning religious people who will gladly tell you who to be and what to do. And each believes they are an expert on your life. But they don't really know you, do they? They can't fully see the mystery of God's unique design in you. That part of you is not a formula but a divine mystery to be explored.

On that note, let me make a promise to you that in this workbook I won't tell you what to do. I won't spoon-feed you answers. I will only offer up a way to find them yourself. This is not an answer book but your personal playbook. It will plumb the depths of your own wisdom and match it with God's truth, and together you will unwind the lame clichés, self-help stupidity and the religious gobbledygook about finding your sacred calling.

Because I've experienced it in my own story, I know the principles of *Wonderlife* can be a dynamic first step to living the life you want. It's an approach that sees each day as a gift and each moment as place to be present. It's a mindset that helps you escape the routine, get unstuck from the muck and see the liberating truth of who you are and what you're made to do.

But a small caution and warning. Don't do this if you're not willing to grow and stretch and challenge yourself. If you don't want to change right now, that's okay. There is a time and season for everything. But do come back when you're ready.

But if you want a *wonderlife*, it will require you to bravely face the devilish lies you've accepted for too long. The lie of control. The lie of victimhood. The lie of fairness. The lie of fear. The lie of shame. Yes, even the lie that you can be anything you want to be. And facing these new truths will require our surrender. As my friend Bob Goff says, "God can't change who we're becoming until we let go of who we were."

So if that's the semi-bad news about this process, then this next idea will be the really great news. Living the *wonderlife* doesn't mean you have to find some "perfect life," but only embrace your current life—your messy, fragile, beautiful, confusing, funky life— filled with the wonder it was made for. This is not self-discovery but actually self-recovery.

I think the truly delicious part of this experience is that you can enjoy the gift of being God's beloved and all of the benefits of that identity. It means you can stop hustling for your self-worth. You don't need to prove anything to anyone anymore. You are not what others have told you, what your heart tells you or what the "powers that be" say you are. You're not your accomplishments or your failures.

Living the *wonderlife* means who you say you are will never overshadow who God says you are. In scripture, Jesus always tells us who we are before He tells us what to do. God says, "You are mine. You are my beloved." And that's enough if you let it be. Father Richard Rohr nails it when he says, "There is nothing to prove and nothing to protect. I am who I am and it's enough."

There is nothing to prove and nothing to protect. I am who I am and it's enough!

In my own story I've come to realize that I am broken. My imperfectness is a part of me. I used to feel shame about this and feared my own story. And through my own struggles and rock-bottom experiences I have learned a powerful truth that has set me free. That the whole point of *absolutely* everything in my life is God wanting to radically love me and be with me. Everything about absolutely everything fits into that simple truth. It is true about my life and it is true about your life too. I believe we come from God, we return to God and everything in between is a lesson in love.

So I want to propose four simple "lifemarks" that will equip you each day to live a life of meaning and purpose. It is a new way of seeing that leads to a new way of being.

These four lifemarks are:

1) I believe my story matters.
2) I am unashamed of what I love and care about.
3) I am honest about my obstacles and opportunities.
4) I am fully present for my life.

So get out your pens and sharpen up your pencils. Get ready to draw and journal and smile. Grab the keys to your locked-up heart, get your friends together and take comfort in the fact that God is not done writing your story. It's time to become your God-made self. Your easiest self. Your deepest and lightest self. It's the *wonderlife*.

- *Johann Wolfgang von Goethe*

I AM NOT AFRAID OF STORMS FOR I
AM LEARNING HOW TO SAIL MY SHIP.

- Louisa May Alcott

every part of my story
makes me who I am —
even the messy parts.

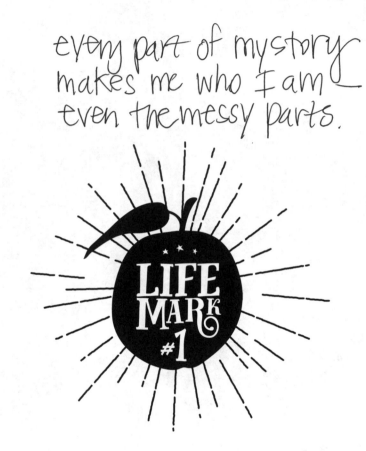

LIFE
MARK
#1

I BELIEVE MY STORY MATTERS

EVERY PART OF MY STORY MAKES ME WHO I AM—
EVEN THE MESSY PARTS.

IF YOU LET ME
SEE THE REAL YOU,
THE DARK AND THE LIGHT,
YOUR WRETCHEDNESS AND GLORY,
YOUR DEPRAVITY AND HOLINESS,
THE UGLY AND THE BEAUTY,
I WOULD FIND YOU
TO BE WONDERFUL.
AND THAT IS GRACE.

You know what the cheapest items at most garage sales are? The books. Stories that took years to create are now strewn among ab-crunchers, musty clothing and DVDs priced at two for a buck. Secondhand stores, thrift shops and garage sales are loaded with books that no one really wants. And so we get the impression they don't matter. Stories are a dime a dozen—and really, who has time to read anymore?

But recently I learned about a small town in France where someone pulled an old, damaged book off a library shelf. It didn't look like anything special. No one had touched the book for two hundred years. But as they cracked open the faded cover and turned past the missing title page, they made a shocking discovery. They held in their hands an original copy of *The Complete Works of William Shakespeare* from 1623. It was incredibly rare. Valued at more than $2 million. A precious piece of history. A treasure.

If you're like me, when you think about your story, you might relate more to the bargain bin book. You think, *I'm nothing special. I have people who love me, but in the overall scheme of things my story isn't that important.* You think your life is the two-for-a-buck variety.

But here's the truth about you. The things that make your story have value are the same things that make the Shakespeare book priceless: the author and the authenticity. The value of your story comes from the person who wrote it and the fact that's it's an original. You may think your story doesn't matter, but God says otherwise. You are incredibly rare. A precious piece of history. A priceless treasure.

So let me ask you a question. Have you grasped the amazing fact that there is no one else like you on the planet? Seriously. Do you understand how original you are? I'm not just talking about your fingerprints or your DNA. I'm taking about your soul. I'm talking about who you are. The things you love. The things that make you smile or blush. The things that make you laugh or cry. Your personality. No matter how you feel about you, God delights in you. He is writing a one-of-a-kind story for you that only you can live. This makes your story and your life priceless!

Don't believe me? Ephesians 2:10 (NLT) says, "For we are God's masterpiece. He has created us anew in Christ Jesus, so we can do the good things he planned for us long ago." You see, God has been thinking about you a lot! Your life is not an afterthought or some cheap story that He quickly threw together one night.

Consider what Psalm 139:16 (NLT) says about you. It declares, "You saw me before I was born. Every day of my life was recorded in your book. Every moment was laid out before a single day had passed."

Face it—you are a one-of-a-kind original. Your story is penned by God Himself. And living the *wonderlife* means that you embrace this fact about who you are and the story that you are a part of. God was thinking about you before you were even born. And that means your story matters, all of it. It matters to Him, so it should matter to you, too. Every single page—even the pages you want to tear out.

So often we feel disqualified by our past. Maybe you have had a series of failures, bad decisions or struggles in your life. Perhaps you feel ashamed of the darkness in your story. But don't despair, my friend. God is present everywhere, even in the darkness. Earlier in Psalm 139 (NIV) the writer says, "Even the darkness will not be dark to you; the night will shine like the day, for darkness is as light to you." He takes our darkness and makes it light. He gives it purpose if we let Him. Or as a friend told me one time, "Darkness exists to make the light count."

God may be the author of our stories, but too often we are the editors. And for that matter—the critics too. We feel too broken to belong. Too messed up to matter. But your mistakes and failures are what give you depth. And authenticity is what makes you priceless. Your past struggles are not a liability—they are your unfair advantage.

Here's what I mean. People may be attracted to your strengths, but they connect to your weaknesses. One of the things that I've discovered is that the words "Me too" are some of the most healing words ever spoken to each other. It is when your struggle connects to someone else's struggle. It is when your pain is similar to a friend's pain. When we say the words "Me too," something sacred happens in that moment. It is in this moment that your story is your authority and your mess becomes your message.

But that requires you to be the you that you were meant to be. It means that we bravely embrace all of our story. No more editing. No more hiding the imperfect parts. Remember, you're not the author, but you get to be the hero who has overcome the difficult seasons of life.

It also means you courageously share the imperfect parts of right now. My friend Blaine Hogan said that if we only tell our story as "I was lost and now I'm found and I've never been lost again," then those are false stories. Those stories do not heal others' hearts. The struggle of the right now matters too. Our current brokenness being mended into wholeness is what allows us to love others well with our here and now story.

For so long, I thought I had to be strong. I believed the lie that said that I could only show healed scars but not open wounds. I practiced bogus authenticity. I mastered carefully orchestrated, controlled vulnerability. I held back my heart because I was scared. Scared of rejection. Scared of losing love. Scared of my right-now wounds. Scared of people thinking I was weak. Maybe you have been here too?

About a year ago a friend helped me see an important truth I had missed along the way. He reminded me that "only broken things can help make broken things beautiful again." Or as author Brennan Manning states, "In love's service, only wounded soldiers can serve." It is in that moment that my whole story became a redeemed weapon of love.

For others, it's not the failures that make us feel like we don't matter, but our wins. All of our successes, the things we were proudest of, have been ignored by others. No one seemed to notice the good things. We feel forgotten. Overlooked. I have seen the hurt of not being recognized swallow up too many friends. Many have stopped living their story because the world never seemed to notice.

Unfortunately, we live in a time when attention and the number of "likes" and how many people "follow" us seems to be the only thing that matters. If enough ears tune in, we assume we are now worth listening to. If enough eyeballs pay attention, we believe we have value.

But what happens if nobody cares? We feel like nobodies. A lot of us have made the mistake of confusing being admired with being adored.

When someone admires you, they are impressed with something you did. People give you temporary value based on your performance. But when someone adores you, they appreciate you for who you are, regardless of what you do. You aren't just given their momentary attention; you are given their lasting love.

One of my favorite promises of the Bible is this verse from Romans 9:25 (MSG). "I'll call nobodies and make them somebodies; I'll call the unloved and make them beloved." The key to living the *wonderlife* is not about trying to earn the world's admiration, but accepting God's adoration. It's to say, "I am just a nobody, loved by the world's greatest Somebody, so I can love other nobodies so they feel like somebodies."

I hope someday you are admired. That would be great, but never forget that in the end your life matters because God adores you. He says, "You are worth far more than my attention. You are worth my life." Your story matters because you matter to Him. You are His masterpiece. You are not bargain-bin material. You are not a nobody. Your story is precious. Because all of it is you.

MAYBE YOUR LIGHT IS A SEED
AND THE DARKNESS THE DIRT,
IN SPITE OF THE UNEVEN ODDS
BEAUTY LIFTS FROM THE EARTH.

-Sleeping At Last

EXPLORE

EXERCISES TO HELP YOU
EXPLORE YOUR STORY

Glue a photo to this page that represents a meaningful part of your story. Describe why this picture is special to you.

. . . .

. . . .

. . . .

(BTW, BE READY TO SHARE THIS PHOTO WITH YOUR GROUP AT YOUR FIRST MEETING.)

WHAT'S YOUR LEMON?

· ·

Write something that was sour or bitter in your story.

WHAT'S YOUR LEMONADE?

. . . .

Write how you can turn that sour event into something useful.

Circle the size of your *emotional energy* right now.

SHORT   **TALL**   **GRANDE**   **VENTI**

Circle the size of your *creative energy* right now.

SHORT   **TALL**   **GRANDE**   **VENTI**

Circle the size of your *physical energy* right now.

SHORT   **TALL**   **GRANDE**   **VENTI**

PERHAPS
THIS IS
THE MOMENT
FOR WHICH
YOU HAVE
BEEN
CREATED.

-Esther 4:14

YOU'RE RIGHT WHERE YOU'RE SUPPOSED TO BE. GOD WRITES ALL THE PAGES IN OUR BOOK AND THIS CHAPTER MIGHT BE THE HIGHLIGHT OR IT MIGHT BE THE LULL, BUT ULTIMATELY, ITS HIS TO WRITE. RELAX INTO IT, FRIEND. THE STORY ISN'T OVER.

-Aedriel Moxley

ME TOO

What struggles have you been through
that others might have also experienced?
Fill in the circles where you can say "Me too!"

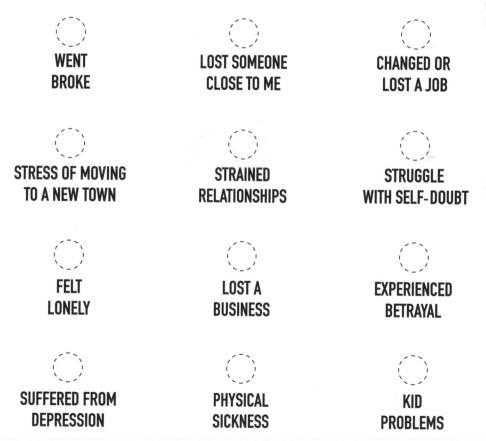

WENT
BROKE

LOST SOMEONE
CLOSE TO ME

CHANGED OR
LOST A JOB

STRESS OF MOVING
TO A NEW TOWN

STRAINED
RELATIONSHIPS

STRUGGLE
WITH SELF-DOUBT

FELT
LONELY

LOST A
BUSINESS

EXPERIENCED
BETRAYAL

SUFFERED FROM
DEPRESSION

PHYSICAL
SICKNESS

KID
PROBLEMS

THE FAMILY
ROOM

THE
KITCHEN

MOM/DAD/
GUARDIAN
BEDROOM

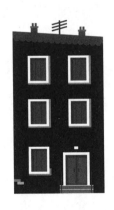

YOUR
BEDROOM

OTHER
ROOMS

THE
YARD

DESCRIBE WHAT IS
HAPPENING IN EACH
ROOM OF THE HOUSE
YOU GREW UP IN.

WHAT EMOTIONS ARE IN THAT ROOM?
WHAT MEMORIES ARE IN THAT ROOM?
HOW DO YOU THINK THAT ROOM HELPED
SHAPE WHO YOU ARE?

ONE OF THE
HAPPIEST
MOMENTS IN LIFE
IS WHEN YOU
FIND THE COURAGE
TO LET GO
OF WHAT YOU
CAN'T CHANGE.

WHAT COLOR HAS YOUR MOOD BEEN LATELY?

Get some crayons and color in the circle that
best represents your current mood.

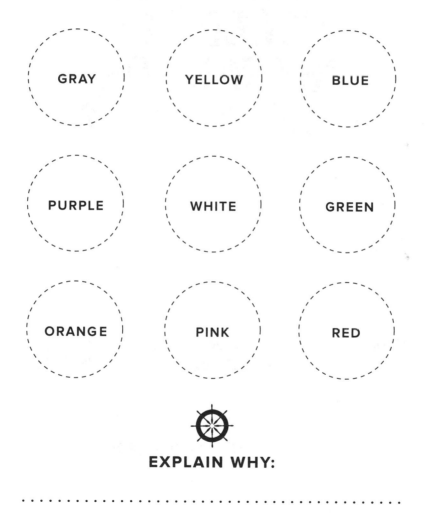

GRAY

YELLOW

BLUE

PURPLE

WHITE

GREEN

ORANGE

PINK

RED

EXPLAIN WHY:

. . . .

. . . .

49

WHAT PRICE WOULD YOU CHARGE FOR YOUR STORY?

A COUPLE BUCKS

○ **AT LEAST TWENTY**

○ **SOME POCKET CHANGE**

○ **SIX FIGURES, BABY!**

○ **A FEW THOUSAND**

○ **MY STORY IS PRICELESS**

WHY DID YOU PICK THAT PRICE?

. . . .

. . . .

NO ONE CAN
MAKE YOU FEEL
INFERIOR WITHOUT
YOUR CONSENT.

- Eleanor Roosevelt

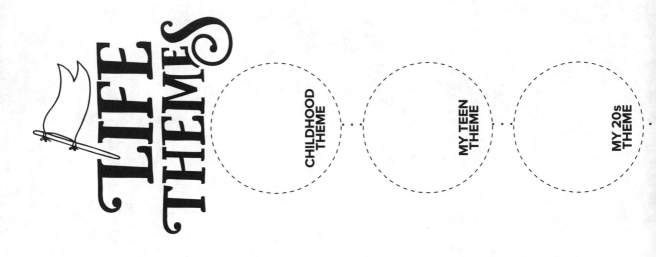

LIFE THEMES

CHILDHOOD THEME

MY TEEN THEME

MY 20s THEME

The complex moments of our stories can
often be summed up with a simple nugget of truth.
Think about the theme of each season of your life.
Write a word or short phrase to describe that theme.
Be raw. Be honest. Say it like it is. Have fun with it!

"So do not fear, for I am with you;
do not be dismayed, for I am your God."
Isaiah 41:10

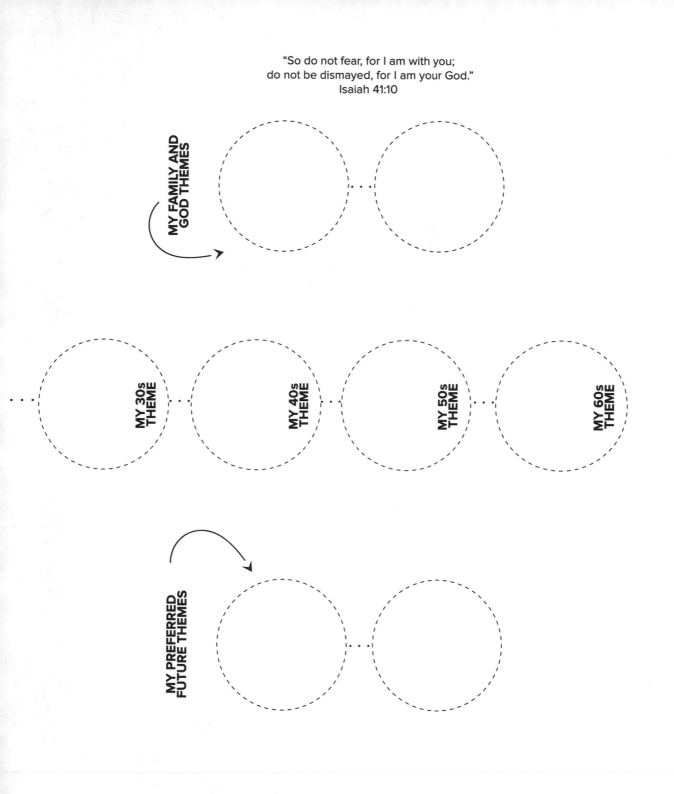

MY FAMILY AND GOD THEMES

MY 30s THEME

MY 40s THEME

MY 50s THEME

MY 60s THEME

MY PREFERRED FUTURE THEMES

FULL PICTURE YOU

"SEE, I AM MAKING
ALL THINGS
NEW."
-Revelation 21:5

WHAT DO YOUR FRIENDS & FAMILY SEE IN YOU?

. . . .

. . . .

WHAT DOES GOD SEE IN YOU?

. . . .

. . . .

WHAT DO YOU SEE IN YOU?

. . . .

. . . .

EINSTEIN'S ROUGH START

Did you know that Albert Einstein wasn't always the Einstein we think of today? He graduated college in 1900 at the bottom of his class. He couldn't find a job. His future looked bleak. Finally, a friend helped Albert land a low-level job at the patent office.

But in spite of this rough start, Einstein never gave up on what he was created to do. Even though he didn't land his dream job, Albert still found time to work on the scientific problems that fascinated him. His work at the patent office would eventually play a key role in Einstein developing his famous formula: $E=mc^2$.

Don't forget you have to start somewhere. For most of us, it starts at the bottom.

Do you believe rough starts can
still find a great ending? Explain.

MEMORY LANE

Write down the very first thought that pops in your mind for each memory. Write one short sentence and then circle if the memory was positive (+) or negative (-).

+ -

AN ELEMENTARY
SCHOOL MEMORY

+ -

YOUR VERY
FIRST MEMORY

+ -

A MEMORY I
WANT TO FORGET

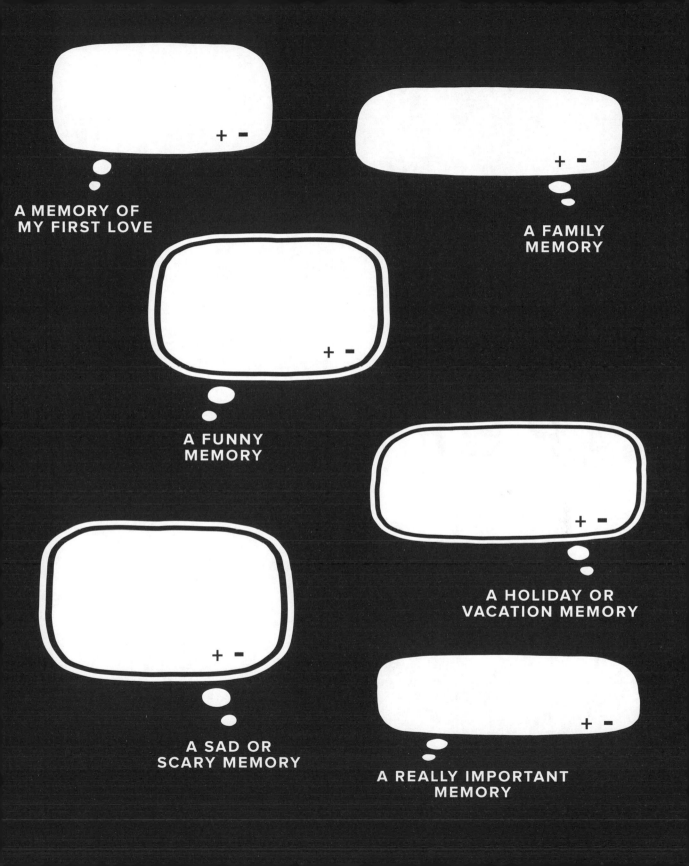

PERFECT IS

SO BORING

So make a big mess on this page! Go for it!

THEY WILL SOAR ON WINGS LIKE EAGLES;
THEY WILL RUN AND NOT GROW WEARY,
THEY WILL WALK AND NOT BE FAINT.

- Isaiah 40:31

TAKE A MOMENT AND GIVE YOURSELF
A SCORE IN EACH AREA. PUT AN X
ON EACH LINE.

SLEEP

1 · 10

FAMILY

1 · 10

GOD STUFF

1 · 10

ATTITUDE

1 · 10

ANGER

1 · 10

HOPE

1 · 10

GROWTH

1 · 10

HEART

1 · 10

HEALTH

1 · 10

WONDERLIFE
BREAKOUT
NUGGET

CHIPS AND CRACKS

Have you heard of wabi-sabi? It's a really cool Japanese idea that says imperfection is beauty. A piece of pottery that's not symmetrical or has a chip is seen as beautiful, not despite its flaw, but because of it.

The same is true of our lives. Our chips and cracks are our wabi-sabi. 2 Corinthians 4:6-7 says that we are like fragile clay pots that contain a light that shines from our hearts. Clay is fragile. It cracks. But each crack and imperfection is just a chance for His light to stream out.

Don't ever apologize for being imperfect. Don't ever be sorry for being a cracked clay pot. His light leaks out through the broken places. So the next time you feel like covering up, just say, "Wabi-sabi."

List a few cracks and chips that
God wants to shine a light through.

REALLY SMART WRITER-TYPES HAVE FIGURED OUT
THAT THERE ARE ONLY SEVEN BASIC TYPES OF STORIES.
CIRCLE THE TYPE OF PLOT THAT BEST REPRESENTS
YOUR STORY. DO YOU LIKE THIS PLOT? EXPLAIN.

OVERCOMING THE MONSTER

This is the classic underdog story like *Rocky*, *Forrest Gump* and *David & Goliath*.

THE QUEST

This is a story about getting from point A to point B. *The Lord of the Rings* is a quest plot.

REBIRTH

This is a story of renewal like the movie *It's a Wonderful Life* or *How the Grinch Stole Christmas*.

THE JOURNEY
AND RETURN

This is a story about transformation while on travel and then returning home. *The Wizard of Oz* is this type of plot.

TRAGEDY

These are stories where the main character has a flaw that leads to tragedy in spite of good intentions. The movie *Titanic* and *Romeo and Juliet* are examples.

RAGS TO
RICHES

Cinderella and *Charles Dickens* and the Eddie Murphy movie *Trading Places* are these type of stories.

COMEDY

The comedy is the opposite of a tragedy and usually has a cheerful ending. Think *Anchorman* or *The Hangover*.

WHAT ARE YOU
LEARNING ABOUT
YOUR STORY?

DO YOU SEE HOW IT
PLAYS AN IMPORTANT
PART IN YOUR LIFE?

ARE THERE PARTS OF
YOUR STORY YOU STILL
WANT TO CHANGE?

FEAR
IS
A
LIAR

. . . .

Write what you're insecure about really tiny on this line.

. . . .

Now write it a little bit bigger here.

. . . .

Good, now write it in all CAPS right here.

NOW WRITE WHAT YOU'RE INSECURE
ABOUT HUMONGOUS ALL OVER
THIS PAGE! GO FOR IT!

"SINCE FEAR IS CRIPPLING, A FEARFUL LIFE—FEAR OF DEATH,
FEAR OF JUDGMENT—IS ONE NOT YET FULLY FORMED IN LOVE."
1 John 4:18

THE GLORY OF YOUR STORY

Think about the word *matter* for a minute. It can mean importance, as in "You matter to me," or it can refer to the physical stuff things are made of. So when you say, "my story matters," it draws on both meanings. Your past is filled with solid things that have weight and depth (just like matter) but God is also infusing your life with significance (making it matter).

Another word that pulls double duty like this is the Hebrew word *kabod*. This word means heavy, weighty or burdensome. But it's also translated as glorious.

I know that's a lot of word talk, but here's the point. Your story is pulling double duty. It may feel like a weight at times, like a burden, but it's also glorious, bright and wonderful. That's part of what it means to matter. It's the glory of your story.

How is your story both weighty and glorious?
Do you see how both matter? Explain.

GROUP UP

MEET WITH YOUR FRIENDS AND TALK
ABOUT WHAT YOU'RE LEARNING

GROUP DISCUSSION QUESTIONS
"I BELIEVE MY STORY MATTERS"
(Approximately 1 hour, 15 minutes)

"Thank you for making me so wonderfully complex! Your
workmanship is marvelous—how well I know it."
- Psalm 139:14, MSG

1. Take some time to introduce yourselves to each other. Use
the photo that you pasted into your workbook on page 39 as a
starting point to share a little about yourself.

2. Turn to page 80 (which is two pages over) and quickly review
the "Group Promise" together. Make sure to sign and date it.

3. As a group, share some of your hopes and desires for the
next few weeks as you go through *Wonderlife*.

**NOW PLAY THE *WONDERLIFE* DVD OR STREAM THE GROUP
VIDEO AT SECONDCHANCE.ORG/VIDEO.**

4. In the video, Mike referred to the C. S. Lewis quote that says, "Hardships often prepare ordinary people for an extraordinary destiny." Do you believe this is true? Have you seen this in your own life?

5. Psalm 139:14 says we are "wonderfully made." How do our disappointments, imperfections and failures fit into this idea?

6. Do you ever feel the need to "hustle for your worthiness"? Do you ever feel the pressure to do something great for God? Where does this pressure come from?

7. Okay. Let's get really honest. If I asked you to name all the things you love, how long would it take to name yourself? Discuss.

GROUP ACTIVITY

Take a group photo. Do one with normal smiles and then do another photo with crazy faces. Have fun with it and then post your photo online using the hashtag #mywonderlife.

ANYONE WHO HAS A DREAM OF HELPING
THE WORLD, ANYONE WHO WANTS
TO MAKE A DIFFERENCE IN PEOPLE'S
LIVES; ARTISTS, DREAMERS, CREATORS,
BUILDERS, ENTREPRENEURS, PASTORS.
ANYONE WHO WANTS TO BE USED BY GOD
MUST BE BROKEN FIRST. YOU SEE, ONLY
BROKEN THINGS CAN HELP MAKE
BROKEN THINGS BEAUTIFUL AGAIN.

Excerpt From Session One Of
The Wonderlife Videos

GROUP PROMISE

I, _____ commit to these promises as a way to make sure that both I and other group members get the most out of our *Wonderlife* group experience.

- [ ] I will be on time, come prepared and show up with my whole heart.

- [ ] I will honor others by keeping what they share in the group private.

- [ ] In our discussions, I will not try to fix people, preach a sermon or give unsolicited advice.

- [ ] I will respect other group members by not gobbling up all the talk time. It's not about me, it's about us.

- [ ] When I share in the group, I will share primarily about myself and not about others.

- [ ] I will trust God and the Holy Spirit to do the work in all of us.

DATE: _____   SIGNATURE: _____

JUMP IN

LET'S TRY SOME STUFF
THIS WEEK

DESIGN YOUR OWN BOOK COVER

Buy a blank journal or notebook this week. Make sure it doesn't have anything fancy on the cover. The more blank it is the better. Now on the cover write a title for the story of your life. Here are a few examples: "Mike's Story," "The Wacky World of Jennifer," or "My Life So Far." You get the point, right? Now draw on the cover with markers and Sharpie pens. Design it however you want. It can just be the title or draw a picture with it too. Be creative. Now consider how you want to fill those blank pages in your book.

HANDLE WITH CARE

It's one thing to believe that our life matters, but it's another to actually treat it that way. Do things this week that demonstrate that you believe God has paid a high price for you. Make decisions that show that you see the value in your story. If you truly believe your life is priceless, then handle it with care. Share how you're doing this with others.

Share online. Use the hashtag:
#MYWONDERLIFE

MY FAVORITE WAY TO

LOVE PEOPLE IS TO IMAGINE

THAT THEIR STORY IS AS MESSY

AS MINE AND IN THAT BEAUTIFUL

MUTUAL MESS, WHAT'S LEFT IS

THE BEST KIND OF LOVE.

LOVE WITHOUT JUDGMENT.

-Aedriel Moxley

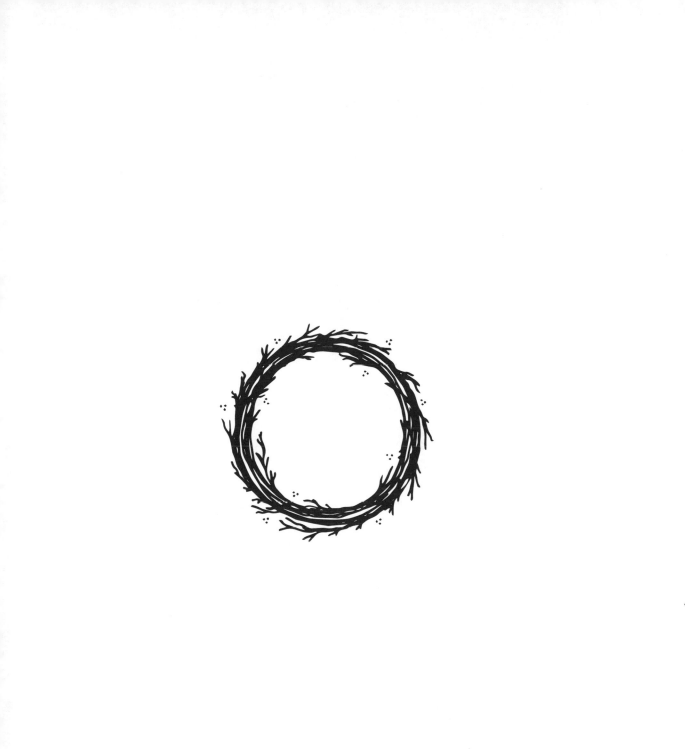

WRITE DOWN THINGS YOU
DON'T WANT TO FORGET HERE.

YOU HAVE SEARCHED ME, LORD,
AND YOU KNOW ME. YOU KNOW
WHEN I SIT AND WHEN I RISE: YOU
PERCEIVE MY THOUGHTS FROM AFAR.
YOU DISCERN MY GOING OUT AND
MY LYING DOWN; YOU ARE FAMILIAR
WITH ALL MY WAYS.

-Psalm 139:1-3

I'M UNASHAMED ABOUT WHAT I LOVE AND CARE ABOUT

I WILL NO LONGER DIMINISH OR DOWNPLAY
MY PASSIONS FOR THE SAKE OF OTHERS' APPROVAL.

THE
MOST
RADICAL
THING
YOU
CAN
BE
IS
YOURSELF.

A few months ago I took my thirteen-year-old daughter to a Taylor Swift concert. She is a raving fan and adores this mega-watt pop superstar. She loves her music and the T-Swift vibe.

At the concert I found myself wedged shoulder to shoulder in a crowd filled with thousands of amped-up junior high girls and twenty-something women. The stadium was swimming in estrogen, femininity and girl power.

Taylor's fans screamed with delight as she sang songs about her mean ex-boyfriends, woman empowerment and how girls should love their bodies no matter what people say. I think she sang a sappy song about Romeo and Juliet, too.

So as a middle-aged man, I gotta admit I was a bit out of place. Okay, maybe *a whole lot* out of place. And you might be thinking, *That must have been really awkward for you, Mike.* Or maybe you believe I was a heroic dad for enduring three non-stop hours of shiny sparkles, glitter and sappy boyfriend-breakup songs. But no, my friends, I am no hero. Because I have a confession. My name is Mike, and I am a full-blown Taylor Alison Swift fan! And just like my teenage daughter, I belong to the "Swiftie" fan club.

That night at the concert I screamed, danced and stood in awe of all things Taylor Swift. I knew every song. I sang every word. It was incredible!

Now, if you think this is stupid and believe that I need to grow up and listen to some "real" music, I have only one thing to say:

Haters gonna hate-hate-hate-hate-hate-hate...
but I'm just gonna shake-shake-shake-shake-shake-shake...
Shake it off. Shake it off.

Seriously, though, one of the biggest obstacles of embracing the *wonderlife* is that you often feel a sense of shame over what you like, love and care about. Somewhere in the story you learned that certain things are okay, adultish and respectable. The critics and nay-sayers created you instead of letting God shape you. Your life was once hot and spicy, but fear watered your story down.

I like how author Jon Acuff warns us to "stop giving haters speaking roles in the movie of our life." He says, "They're just extras." But it happens so often, doesn't it? A rude online comment. Co-workers snickering about your ideas. Being bullied for your passions. And all of a sudden we no longer are our true selves.

We start doing things we are supposed to do rather than things we really like. Sure, we fit in, but we totally lose out. The world likes to bash the weird right out of us, but it's our weird that makes us wonderful.

So let me ask you a question. What fired you up as a kid? Did you love to create stories, explore new places or play house? Did you like to give gifts, collect bugs or make clothes? Think of what you used to do for free, for fun, before the eye-roll police came along. Often it's these baked-in passions and preferences that point toward who you really are and why you're really here. The original kid stuff that you loved is actually a good indicator of the God passions that he originally put inside of you.

When I was a kid, I loved Hot Wheels, Star Wars action figures and pretty much anything else that was fodder for my imagination. I was a feeler and an introvert. I was fascinated by seemingly insignificant things. Other kids were brave and active, but my heart was quiet and sensitive. I cried a lot in public places, and of course when my mom took me to see the movie *ET*. I was a misfit who lived in my little inner world that very few people understood or visited. In a world that only knows how to value brains, beauty, brawn and bucks, I came up *waaaaaaaay* short.

But then I found out God loved me and had a plan for quiet Mike. In fact, God had this super big, serious thing known as a "calling" for me. (Insert angel choir here.) I had been bequeathed a divine purpose. If I could drum up enough faith and do enough spiritual inventory tests, and really get excited about the idea of suffering in a third world country, I could discover this high and holy calling!

The problem is, I never felt high and holy. I eat hot dogs from

7-Eleven. I like super hero movies and the French horn. As far as I could tell, geekiness and crying are not spiritual gifts. I loved such small and simple things; they didn't seem to line up with any huge godly vision.

The pressure to be significant was overwhelming and honestly made me feel like a misfit with God. Even He wanted me to be someone I wasn't. I thought, *If God has a calling for me, either I didn't hear it or I didn't want it, because I'm way more excited about the people I love and the things I love to do.*

But here's what I've learned. The things that I really love to do *are my calling*. They are your calling too. Our deepest passions pull us toward God, not away. It's not about having a "God sized" dream but loving the dream God already put inside of us.

Here's what I mean. The word *calling* comes from the Greek word *vocare,* which basically means, "Hey, you! Come over here." Passion is the pull of God calling your name. He picks you because of all your likes, quirks and interests, not in spite of them.

There are certain things in this world that only you can care about. And guess what? God calls you to care about them. There are certain jobs in this world that only you can do, and God calls you to do them. These little things may turn into big things, but they probably won't start that way. They will start with you saying, "I think I can help here." Or "Yeah, I'd like to do that." Or "Yep, that sounds like my thing."

YOU DON'T NEED A

Permission Slip

TO LOVE THE THINGS

GOD HAS PUT

INSIDE OF YOU.

Calling is God seeing a weird, quirky need with your name written all over it and saying, "Hey, you! You're going to like this."

The reason I missed my calling for so long is that it sounded too much like what I already loved to do. I'm convinced that if most of us saw what God really expected of us, our first reaction would not be "Wow, that's so huge!" It would be "But that seems so easy. It seems exactly like what I want to do." By the way, it is also these very things that the eye-roll police would never approve of.

When Jesus calls out, saying, "Come to me all who are weary and need rest," and offers His "light and easy yoke," those words basically mean a custom fit. A yoke was a collar you put on an animal to pull things, and the owner took great care to fit it to the animal's neck. He wanted to reduce the irritation and maximize the pulling power. That is what God wants for you: rest. Not the kind of rest that kicks up its feet and sleeps the day away, but the kind of rest that says, "I was made for this!"

One of the best spiritual acts of renewal we can do is to be honest about what we really care about. The way to live the *wonderlife* is to say, "I will no longer diminish or downplay my passions for the sake of others' approval. I will trust what God has placed inside of me." Remember, people can only shame you if you let them.

But no one cares about what I like—shake it off.
But it doesn't seem spiritual enough—shake it off.
But it doesn't feel big, important or popular enough—shake it off.

It's important to remember God has trouble blessing the fake version of you. He can't call you to the passions you ignore or deny. So get honest! What do you really care about? What means the world to you even though others don't really understand? Pay attention to those things and you will start to hear God's voice saying, "Hey, you—yeah you. Come here. I have a little thing only you can do."

It might not make you famous, but it will make you faithful. It might not change the world, but it will change you. You are here to live a life that makes your heart come alive. And the world won't be complete until you do.

So here's to smaller callings and freer hearts. God loves the weird that makes you wonderful.

EXPLORE

EXERCISES TO HELP YOU
EXPLORE YOUR STORY

WE ARE ALL

Rough Drafts

OF WHO WE
ARE BECOMING.

—

-BOB GOFF

WHAT CHOPS DOWN YOUR DREAMS?

Circle the stumps that apply or write a few of your own.

FEAR CRITICS FAILURES

MY PAST BUSYNESS FINANCES

BAD LUCK NO PLAN APATHY

EXPLAIN HOW & WHY:

. . . .

. . . .

DEFINING PRIORITIES

My Most Important Personal Value

- -

My Most Important Family Value

- -

My Most Important Spiritual Value

- -

My Most Important Relationship Value

- -

My Most Important Financial Value

- -

Is your life currently aligned with
your most important values?

YES   NO   KINDA

"SOMEDAY" STUFF

Circle items you've been putting off
in your life. Also, jot down other
"someday stuff" on this page.

START A BLOG

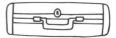

**GROW A
MUSTACHE**

**DEVELOP A
NEW IDEA**

TRAVEL

**STUDY
PHOTOGRAPHY**

**GIVE MY LIFE
TO GOD**

**CALL AN
OLD FRIEND**

. . . .
OTHER SOMEDAY STUFF

**RESPECT
MYSELF MORE**

**A ROAD TRIP
WITH FRIENDS**

**CHANGE MY
HAIRSTYLE**

**START
EXERCISING**

WRITE A SONG

**WRITE A
BOOK**

LEARN TO COOK

**SHARE MY
HEART MORE**

WHAT STEP WOULD HELP YOU TO START NOW?

. . . .

. . . .

REJECTING CONFORMITY

A lot of us are scared to trust God because we think He'll ruin our personality. But God loves variety. Just look at nature. Do we really need 400,000 different species of beetle? God thinks so.

It's actually culture that tries to crush variety and make you fit a mold. Buy this to be happy. Wear this to fit in. Do this to be popular. They tell you be a second-rate version of someone else rather than a first-rate version of yourself.

But God says to reject conformity by embracing transformation. Romans 12:2 says, "Do not be conformed to this world, but be transformed by the renewal of your mind." In the end you have two choices: be conformed to the shape culture says is valuable or be transformed by God and embrace the value He planted in you to begin with. One is a clone. The other is the weird and wonderful you.

Right now, do you feel like you're being transformed by God or being conformed to the world? Explain.

YOU KNOW ME INSIDE AND OUT,
YOU KNOW EVERY BONE IN MY
BODY; YOU KNOW EXACTLY
HOW I WAS MADE, BIT BY BIT,
HOW I WAS SCULPTED FROM
NOTHING INTO SOMETHING.

-Psalm 139:15

LIKES & DISLIKES

List below the things you "love to do" and "loathe to do."
How can knowing both help you be who God
created you to be?

THINGS I LOVE

· ·

· ·

· ·

· ·

· ·

THINGS I LOATHE

· ·

· ·

· ·

· ·

· ·

SECRET IDENTITY

List your secret characteristics that most people don't know about you. And just for fun, cut out this secret identity and try it on.

My Secret Talent Is:

- -

My Hidden Passion Is:

- -

My Super Secret Super Power Is:

- -

Most People Would Never Guess That:

- -

My Secret Strength Is:

- -

THE THIEF COMES ONLY TO STEAL
AND KILL AND DESTROY; I HAVE
COME THAT THEY MAY HAVE LIFE.
-*John 10:10*

LABELS LIE

Have you ever bought something that was mislabeled? Most of the time it's just an inconvenience. If you have an allergy, it can be more serious. But here's a truth I want to point out: when something is mislabeled, the product doesn't lie—the label does.

If it says "lemon pie" on the box and apple pie comes out, then the apple pie is true and the lemon label is false. You're like, "Well, duh, Mike! That's pretty obvious!" But here's the thing. When someone labels you or me, we tend to think the label is correct and the product is wrong.

But you are not your labels, because labels lie. No matter how many times you are slid into a lemon box, you are still the apple pie that comes out. A French apple with all the crumbles on top ready to be served up warm with a side of ice cream.

So who are you really? Perhaps that is what we need to discover. But we know this one thing to be true about you—you are not your labels.

What labels have others tried to put on you
that are not true or accurate? Explain.

MY LIFE MANIFESTO

A manifesto is a published declaration of intentions, motives or views about something. Think of it as your mission statement for your life. Fill in the blanks.

I AM.....................

GOD IS.....................

AND TOGETHER WE ARE:

....

WHAT WOULD YOU DO IF
MONEY WERE NO OBJECT?

TALK ABOUT IT AND
DRAW IT HERE.

WHAT
MESSAGES
ARE THE
TAPES IN
YOUR HEAD
PLAYING
THESE
DAYS?

ARE THEY POSITIVE OR NEGATIVE?

CAN GOD HELP CHANGE
THE TAPES?

WRITE THE MESSAGES ON THE CASSETTE
TAPES ON THE NEXT PAGE.

PASSION VS. PASTIME

When we talk about passion, a lot of people confuse it with a pastime. For instance, they like to watch TV, go out to eat or relax on the beach. They say "My passion is just hanging out and taking it easy." I love all those things too, but they are not passions.

The word *passion* comes from a Latin word meaning, "to suffer." True passions are things so important to you that you are willing to suffer for them. I enjoy food, but I have a passion for helping people. I like coffee, but I have a passion for creating. I like a good movie, but I'm willing to suffer for my family.

Passions are the powerful forces that drive us. Often passions come at a high price. Pastimes are what refresh us when our passions deplete us. Knowing the difference can really impact the direction of your life.

What passions are you willing to suffer for?
List some on this page.

SINCE THIS IS THE KIND OF LIFE WE HAVE CHOSEN, THE LIFE OF THE SPIRIT, LET US MAKE SURE THAT WE DO NOT JUST HOLD IT AS AN IDEA IN OUR HEADS OR A SENTIMENT IN OUR HEARTS, BUT WORK OUT ITS IMPLICATIONS IN EVERY DETAIL OF OUR LIVES. THAT MEANS WE WILL NOT COMPARE OURSELVES WITH EACH OTHER AS IF ONE OF US WERE BETTER AND ANOTHER WORSE. WE HAVE FAR MORE INTERESTING THINGS TO DO WITH OUR LIVES. EACH OF US IS AN ORIGINAL.

-Galatians 5:25-26, MSG

GROUP UP

MEET WITH YOUR FRIENDS AND TALK
ABOUT WHAT YOU'RE LEARNING

GROUP DISCUSSION QUESTIONS
"I AM UNASHAMED ABOUT WHAT I LOVE AND CARE ABOUT"

(Approximately 1 hour, 15 minutes)

"For you created my inmost being;
you knit me together in my mother's womb."
Psalm 139:13 NIV

1. Take some time to discuss the exercises, breakouts and reading from your workbook. Share some of your insights from this week. What was your favorite exercise? What surprised you? What challenged you? What have you discovered about God and yourself this week?

2. Why do you think we are so concerned about others' opinions? Why are approval and acceptance such powerful forces in our life?

3. Have you ever held back a dream, passion or idea because you thought it might be unpopular? Discuss.

NOW PLAY THE *WONDERLIFE* DVD OR STREAM THE GROUP VIDEO AT SECONDCHANCE.ORG/VIDEO.

4. Mike shared that being a "people-pleaser" or being an "over-explainer" and playing "success theater" undermines our *wonderlife*. Which of these is your greatest struggle?

5. Share something weird, funky or quirky that most people don't know about you. Did God knit together our quirkiness too?

6. Romans 12:2 says, "Don't copy the behavior and customs of this world." Why is it so easy to let the world influence who we are becoming?

7. Share a moment from your story when you encountered the "eye-roll police." How did it make you feel? How can we as a community build others' dreams versus harshly critiquing them? Do you think God ever rolls his eyes?

GROUP ACTIVITY

Pair up with one other person in the group and commit to text or email them this week with a word of encouragement. Nothing fancy. Just a few sentences.

SO DON'T LET YOUR PASSIONS BE
SHAPED BY OTHERS' PREFERENCES.
LET GOD'S LOVE DO THAT. THAT'S
WHY I SAY, "YOUR PASSIONS DON'T
NEED APOLOGIES, THEY NEED
CHEERLEADERS."

*Excerpt from Session Two of the
Wonderlife videos*

JUMP IN

LET'S TRY SOME STUFF
THIS WEEK

WEAR YOUR WEIRD

This week, wear a quirky piece of clothing or a weird hat or accessory that you normally wouldn't go out in public in. Or take a risk and go against your normal wardrobe or hairstyle choices and mix it up a little. Wear your weird and see how people react. Is it positive or negative? How many people noticed? How did you feel being just you? Btw, take a photo and tag it #mywonderlife so we can see it too!

LET YOUR MIND WANDER

Take a few minutes at the close of each day and let your thoughts transport you back to your childhood. Think of an activity you loved to do when you were a kid. Do your best to tap into the feelings you felt in that moment. Try to picture what is going on and why it made you so happy. Write that activity out and think about how you could incorporate it into your current life.

Share online. Use the hashtag:
#MYWONDERLIFE

WRITE DOWN THINGS YOU
DON'T WANT TO FORGET HERE.

I'M HONEST ABOUT MY OBSTACLES AND OPPORTUNITIES

I LIVE AUTHENTICALLY AND HUMBLY WITH THE
TRUTH OF WHO I AM AND HOW GOD CREATED ME.

ALL GREAT SPIRITUALITY
TEACHES ABOUT LETTING GO OF
WHAT YOU DON'T NEED AND
WHO YOU ARE NOT. AT THAT
PLACE, YOU WILL HAVE NOTHING
TO PROVE TO ANYBODY
AND NOTHING
TO PROTECT.

-Richard Rohr

Kids are great at dreaming big dreams. Ask them what they want to be when they grow up, and you will hear things like firefighter, doctor or a combination of a veterinary-mermaid-rock star. Kids don't let little things like reality limit their potential.

When I was kid I believed I could be Michael Jordan. I thought I could accomplish this through following three simple steps. All I had to do was:

Step 1: Convince my parents to buy me Air Jordans.
Step 2: Shave my head.
Step 3: Be 6' 6" tall.

Three simple steps to becoming Michael Jordan!

My idea of becoming Michael Jordan lines up perfectly with a current narrative of culture: you can be anything you want to be. If you can dream it, you can achieve it. I believe I can fly. I believe I can touch the sky. Ask the universe for whatever you want. There are no limits!

And though that sounds incredible, here's the honest truth: you can't be anything you want to be; you can only be who God made you to be.

Now you might be saying to yourself, *Hey, Mike, don't rain on my parade. Don't be dumping on my dream*. Hearing this truth might make you mad. It may feel like I'm saying that your dreams don't matter. Not at all. What I am saying is that God's dream matters more. And His dream frees you to be who you really are rather than who you think you need to be.

So on the one hand it feels limiting to learn you can never "spread your wings and fly away" if you just believe in yourself enough. But on the other hand, what a relief! All the insane pressure of expectations we put on ourselves to be the next Beyoncé, Michael Jordan or a rockstar mermaid are now gone.

But this also means you are responsible—solely responsible—for becoming the person you *are* meant to be. God does the designing but we do the living. Thomas Merton, who wrote a lot about what it means to enjoy life with God, said this:

"You do not need to know precisely what is happening, or exactly where it is all going. What you need is to recognize the possibilities and challenges offered by the present moment, and to embrace them with courage, faith and hope."

That's why we need to get clear about our obstacles and our opportunities. We work with the gifts God gives us rather than scrambling to get the abilities and opportunities we think will make us happy.

In Ephesians 1:18 (NIV) the Apostle Paul said, "I pray that the eyes of your heart may be enlightened in order that you may know the hope to which he has called you." In order for us to have our "eyes enlightened" to the obstacles and opportunities, it will require three things from us: honesty, humility and help.

Honesty: First, we need to take a fearless inventory of our lives. We should never be afraid to look in the mirror. An eyes-wide-open-no-holds-barred gut check can do wonders for our *wonderlife*. Ask yourself a few questions. What do my past successes and failures tell me about who I am and what I want? What am I really chasing? Is my pursuit of my impossible dream just my current plan to get the love I desire?

Humility: Next, we need to humble ourselves and get comfy in our own purpose. And that means blowing up our current definitions of what truly matters. Size, scale or pop-culture importance might be important to us but not to God. The ministry of guacamole making, warm hug giving and packing kids' lunches is just as significant as fighting the evils of human trafficking. You may not think so, but God does. He never called us to be famous, only faithful.

Help: Finally, we have to realize we need each other. We all have blind spots that we won't be able to see on our own—that's why they are called blind spots. Right now, I bet you have some things in your life that are holding you back. Supportive friends can help you identify them. But friends don't just help identify our biggest flaws but also remind us of our greatest strengths. Strengths that we often forget about or fail to recognize.

So let me ask you a question. Do you know what the most destructive kind of lies are? Well, here is what I've discovered—the most destructive lies are the lies that we tell ourselves. They keep us locked into a life we were never created for. A boring life. A stuck life. A life of quiet despair. And you know what I finally realized in my own life? The lies I tell myself make perfect sense to me every single time. And that's why it's so easy for me to believe them. My own lies are exactly what Mike Foster wants to hear and they validate everything I want to believe.

Unfortunately, our lies wear us out by pursuing goals that God never meant for us to chase. A pipe-dream life. Unreal and unattainable. Both are not us. The lies must die so you can finally live. I love what author Paulo Coelho encourages us to do when he says, "Close some doors today. Not because of pride, incapacity or arrogance, but simply because they lead you nowhere."

I don't know if you've ever had a wart frozen off before, but it is a grisly process. These suckers don't belong on your skin, but they are a part of you, and they need to go. So a doctor torches it with -321 degrees liquid nitrogen. It burns. A lot. Then they do it some more. And some more. It hurts the whole time. But the wart does not freeze and shatter like you see on TV—it just dies. And hurts.

For weeks. It gets grosser and blacker each day, but eventually you look down and the thing has fallen off.

That's what it's like to lose the extra parts of ourselves — the dreams and desires that don't belong. They are a part of us, but they are not us. They burn and hurt and die a slow, painful death. We are more ourselves when the warts are gone. There is no gentle way to kill off a part of you. Death always feels like death, but God assures us there is always life on the other side.

Some people think life is like a car. If you have enough gas and a map, you can get wherever you want. Destination is all about determination. They want to win, warts and all.

We celebrate people who do just this. We idolize athletes who make it big, artists who reach the top and business icons who achieve success. They all tell us the same thing: dream big, work hard and drive your way to the good life. And don't forget to ask God for some gas every once in a while.

But I've found life is more like a sailboat. You can have a destination in mind, but you'll never get there if you don't pay attention to the wind. The wind is the key to everything. Your job is not to paddle—that is a last resort. Your job, if you choose to accept it, is to catch the wind. And once you raise the sails, you need to steer the boat.

Sometimes the wind is at your back and it's easy. Other times the wind is against you. But good sailors know that if you angle the boat slightly, you can still catch the wind and move forward. But in the end, sailing is not so much about the destination but the journey.

That's what the *wonderlife* is all about: To show up each day and align your life to the Wind-giver. It's about dropping the oars of self-sufficiency, shutting off the engine of self-centeredness and focusing on how God is using your life to bring His love into the world.

You can't be anything you want to be. Sorry, it's true. But you can be who God made you to be. Your dreams may be limited by your obstacles and opportunities, but your life is empowered by God's love and imagination. His dreams are way better than anything we can dream up and His plans for us are always good.

THE
JOURNEY
ISN'T ABOUT BECOMING
ANYTHING. IT'S ABOUT

EVERYTHING THAT
REALLY ISN'T YOU.

SHOW UP.

BE BRAVE.

Live Your Story

SMILE WHILE

YOU DO IT.

BUT THE IDEA THAT EVERYTHING WE DO IS PART OF THE PURSUIT OF HAPPINESS SEEMS TO ME A REALLY DANGEROUS IDEA AND HAS LED TO A CONTEMPORARY DISEASE IN WESTERN SOCIETY, WHICH IS FEAR OF SADNESS. WE'RE KIND OF TEACHING OUR KIDS THAT HAPPINESS IS THE DEFAULT POSITION - IT'S RUBBISH. WHOLENESS IS WHAT WE OUGHT TO BE STRIVING FOR AND PART OF THAT IS SADNESS, DISAPPOINTMENT, FRUSTRATION, FAILURE; ALL OF THOSE THINGS WHICH MAKE US WHO WE ARE. HAPPINESS AND VICTORY AND FULFILLMENT ARE NICE LITTLE THINGS THAT ALSO HAPPEN TO US, BUT THEY DON'T TEACH US MUCH. I'D LIKE JUST FOR A YEAR TO HAVE A MORATORIUM ON THE WORD "HAPPINESS" AND TO REPLACE IT WITH THE WORD "WHOLENESS." ASK YOURSELF "IS THIS CONTRIBUTING TO MY WHOLENESS?" AND IF YOU'RE HAVING A BAD DAY, IT IS.

-Hugh Mackay

(Highlight or underline the parts of this quote that you like or perhaps disagree with.)

EXPLORE

EXERCISES TO HELP YOU
EXPLORE YOUR STORY

THIS IS
AN OFFICIAL
REST STOP.

BREATHE.
COUNT TO TEN.
PRAY.
LET
THE
WORRY
GO.
REPEAT AS
NECESSARY.

PEOPLE I LOOK UP TO

Write down the names of 3 people you respect and look up to. List the traits and characteristics that you admire in them.

PERSON #1

. . . .

REASON WHY:

. . . .

. . . .

PERSON #2

. . . .

REASON WHY:

. . . .

. . . .

PERSON #3

. . . .

REASON WHY:

. . . .

. . . .

WHAT DO YOU NEED TO LET GO?

Some things were not meant for
you to carry. They are just too heavy.
What do you need to release to God right now?
Write it in the balloon.

SINCE GOD CARES FOR YOU, LET HIM CARRY

ALL YOUR BURDENS AND WORRIES.

-1 Peter 5:7 (VOICE)

GUT CHECK

Answer the questions on the next page by placing an X on the line to describe whether these things are in a good or bad place.

HOW'S YOUR HEART?

🙁 .... 🙂

HOW'S YOUR MIND?

🙁 .... 🙂

HOW'S IT GOING?

🙁 .... 🙂

HOW'S YOUR HOPE?

🙁 .... 🙂

HOW'S YOUR ATTITUDE?

🙁 .... 🙂

COMMENT ON ONE OF YOUR ANSWERS:

....

WE CAME FROM GOD
AND WE RETURN TO GOD
AND
Everything

IN BETWEEN IS A LESSON
IN LOVE

MY PERSONAL
BOARD OF DIRECTORS

Create your own personal board of directors.
Write the name of a person in your life who
could fit each description.

THE COACH

. . . .

This person encourages you when you're
down and helps you figure out solutions.

THE CONNECTOR

. . . .

This person knows a lot of people and can
help make introductions to new relationships.

THE CHEERLEADER

. . . .

This person loves to encourage and will cheer
you in bad seasons and good ones too.

THE CHALLENGER

. . . .

This person won't allow you to lie to yourself and boldly
calls you to do your best. They can be harsh, but still loving.

THE THREE STAGES OF MATURITY

Stage 1: Dependence
When we are born into the world, we are completely dependent on others for everything. We need to be fed, changed and bathed. As we get older, we take over more responsibility. Sometimes this stalls out in the junior high years, but eventually we learn to live on our own in stage two.

Stage 2: Independence
When the day comes that we are living in our own home and we're buying our own stuff, we call this independence. In America we love our independence! And independence is great! It's way better than relying on others to meet our basic needs. But this is not the pinnacle for humans.

Stage 3: Interdependence
This is what happens when independent people come together and rely on each other to achieve greater things. Marriage is interdependence. So are families, businesses and churches. You need people in your life to achieve your greatest potential. That's how God set it up.

What stage of maturity are you in right now?
Do you see the importance of interdependence? Explain.

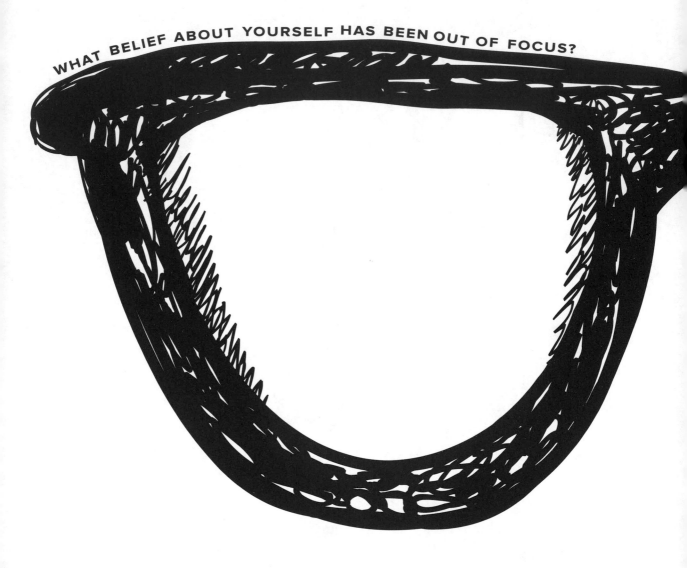

WHAT BELIEF ABOUT YOURSELF HAS BEEN OUT OF FOCUS?

HOW HAS THIS HURT YOUR LIFE? EXPLAIN.

See how long it takes you
to find the black bear paw on this
page. Sometimes it is difficult to find
things even when you know what
you're looking for. It takes real focus
and sometimes a little help from a friend.

ELECTRONICS	DETAILS	SERVING
ACADEMICS	PATIENCE	DECORATING
CREATING	COOKING	BAKING
LEADERSHIP	I'M FLEXIBLE	SMILING
PEOPLE STUFF	COMPUTERS	ORGANIZING
CLARITY	DISCERNMENT	TEAMWORK
SHARING	WISDOM	DEDICATION
SELLING	PAINTING	SINGING
WORK ETHIC	GARDENING	ENCOURAGING
MATH	KID STUFF	LOYALTY
SPORTS	STYLING	SENSING
LISTENING	BIG IDEAS	CONFIDENCE
STORIES	NUMBERS	ENTHUSIASM
CAR STUFF	ADVICE	PROBLEM SOLVING

Take some time and sort the things that you're kinda good at and the things that you're seriously awesome at. It's important to know the difference. There's a short list of possible stuff on the other page to get you started.

THINGS I'M KINDA GOOD AT...BUT NOT REALLY

. . . .

. . . .

. . . .

. . . .

. . . .

THINGS I TOTALLY ROCK EVERY TIME! BAM!

. . . .

. . . .

. . . .

. . . .

. . . .

PLAY VS. WORK

Dallas Willard once defined employment as "the creation of value." It means there was nothing but chaos, emptiness or need and then you happened. And now there is order, fullness and met needs. Employment is a very important part of our identity. We were made to be value-makers. He went on to say that employment can be work or play—the difference is that play is the creation of value that is not necessary.

Some people have natural abilities to create things we need: food, education, child rearing—you name it. Others have natural abilities to create things that are not required: songs, stories, art, jewelry or cupcakes. But both have incredible value. Both are awesome. One set of skills makes life possible, the other gives life value.

What type of value do you love to create?
Work or play? Explain.

The Christian is not the noble anti-hero luxuriating in despair but the child of the kingdom, the grace-merry person who blends the perils of human freedom with the pursuing grace of God. She does not deny evil but installs it in the movement of hope. In her life, as in all life, there are tears and laughter, but ultimately there is laughter, the laughter of the resurrected Christ.

-John Shea

(Highlight or underline the parts of this quote that resonate with you.)

IMPERFECT MOMENTS INVENTORY

God doesn't need us to be perfect. He just wants our imperfections to bring us closer to Him. Circle the imperfect things you've done or write your own. Then color that circle in with a red crayon or marker representing that it is completely forgiven.

NOT SHOWERED FOR A WEEK

SELF-MEDICATED MY PAIN

BROKE A PROMISE TO MYSELF

SAID SOMETHING I DIDN'T MEAN

LOST FAITH IN GOD

SPILLED SOMETHING ON MY SHIRT

TAKEN SOMETHING THAT WASN'T MINE

FILED FOR BANKRUPTCY

HID
SOMETHING
IMPORTANT

SENT A TEXT TO
THE WRONG PERSON

BLAMED SOMEONE
FOR MY PROBLEMS

TRIPPED ON THE
SIDEWALK

ATE TOO MUCH
PIZZA

LIED TO A
GOOD FRIEND

HURT
MYSELF ON
PURPOSE

BLEW UP
AT MY KIDS

QUIT
ON MYSLEF

LOST MY
TEMPER

WHAT'S THE MOST IMPORTANT THING YOU'VE LEARNED FROM YOUR IMPERFECTNESS?

- -

WRITE A LETTER TO YOUR YOUNGER SELF

What would you say?
Any advice? Warnings?
What does your younger
self need to hear right now?

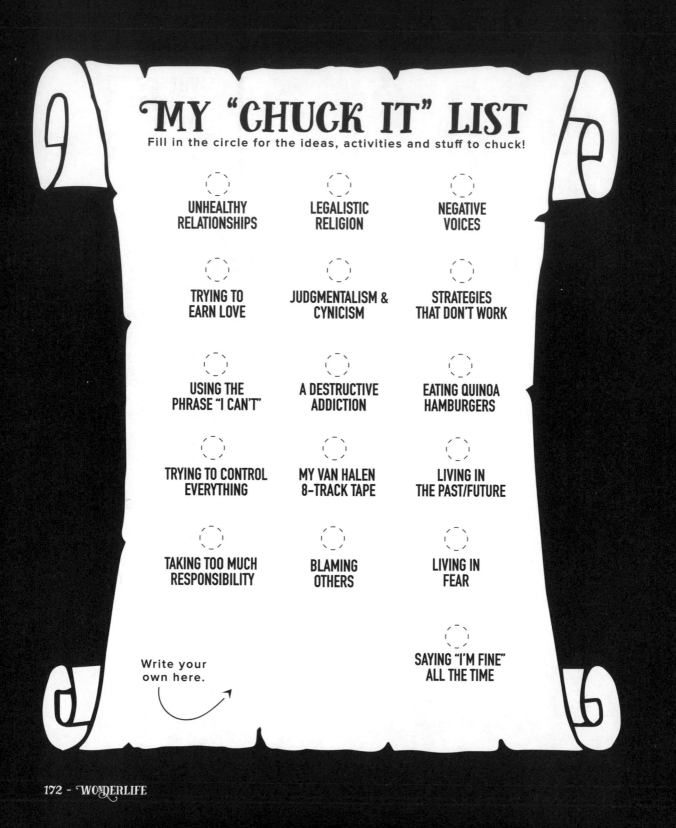

MY "CHUCK IT" LIST

Fill in the circle for the ideas, activities and stuff to chuck!

○ UNHEALTHY RELATIONSHIPS

○ LEGALISTIC RELIGION

○ NEGATIVE VOICES

○ TRYING TO EARN LOVE

○ JUDGMENTALISM & CYNICISM

○ STRATEGIES THAT DON'T WORK

○ USING THE PHRASE "I CAN'T"

○ A DESTRUCTIVE ADDICTION

○ EATING QUINOA HAMBURGERS

○ TRYING TO CONTROL EVERYTHING

○ MY VAN HALEN 8-TRACK TAPE

○ LIVING IN THE PAST/FUTURE

○ TAKING TOO MUCH RESPONSIBILITY

○ BLAMING OTHERS

○ LIVING IN FEAR

○ SAYING "I'M FINE" ALL THE TIME

Write your own here. ↷

I CAN MAKE IT THROUGH ANYTHING IN
THE ONE WHO MAKES ME WHO I AM.
-*Apostle Paul*

CLOUDS AND THE GROUND

Some people live with their head in the clouds. They are the dreamers and the possibility-addicts. They see so much potential in everything and are always full of ideas. The problem is that they never get traction on anything. Their head is in the clouds but their feet never touch the ground.

Then there are people who are grounded. They don't waste time daydreaming. They meet needs. They are practical. But often these folks live small lives. They complete their lists, even when the lists cease to even matter. Their feet are on the ground, but their heads are too. They have no dreams, only routines.

The sweet spot is to live with your head in the clouds *and* your feet on the ground. It means to dream of possibilities and take practical steps to get there. Every dream comes with a routine and every routine needs a dream. Without both, we end up either stuck on the ground or floating to nowhere.

Which way do you need to stretch? Toward
the clouds or the ground? Explain.

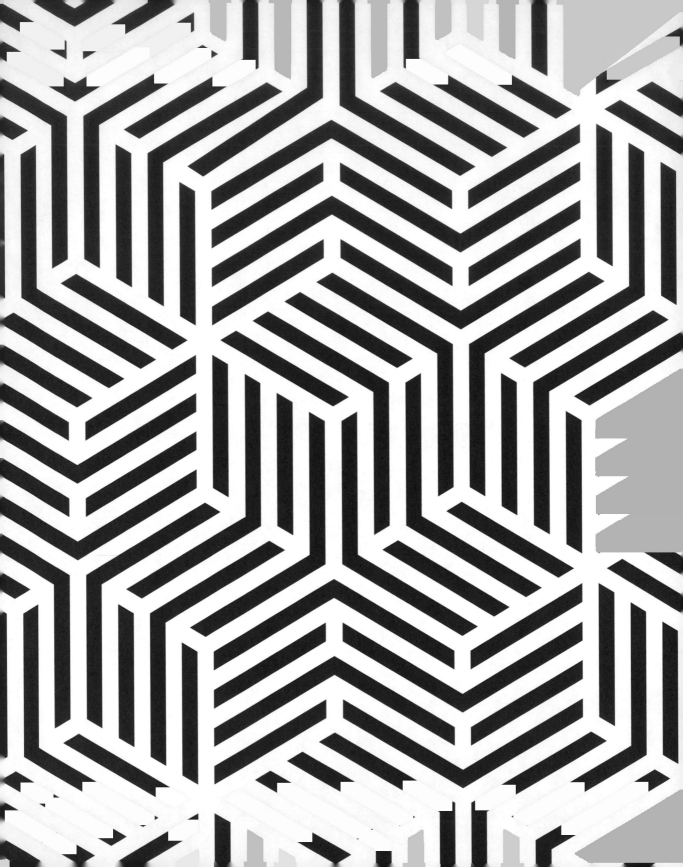

I HAVE SET THE LORD ALWAYS BEFORE ME.

BECAUSE HE IS AT MY RIGHT HAND,

I WILL NOT BE SHAKEN.

-Psalm 16:8

GROUP UP

MEET WITH YOUR FRIENDS AND TALK
ABOUT WHAT YOU'RE LEARNING

GROUP DISCUSSION QUESTIONS
"I'M HONEST ABOUT MY OBSTACLES AND OPPORTUNITIES"

(Approximately 1 hour 15 minutes)

"See if there is any offensive way in me,
and lead me in the way everlasting."
- Psalm 139:24, NIV

1. Take some time to discuss the exercises, breakouts and reading from your workbook. Share some of your insights from this week. What was your favorite exercise? What surprised you? What challenged you? What have you discovered about God and yourself this week?

2. Why, as a culture, do you think we are uncomfortable with the idea of having limits?

NOW PLAY THE *WONDERLIFE* DVD OR STREAM THE GROUP VIDEO AT SECONDCHANCE.ORG/VIDEO.

3. Why do people often feel disillusioned about how life is turning out? Have you ever felt this way before?

4. Mike quoted author Cheryl Strayed, who said, "You don't have a right to the cards you believe you should have been dealt, but you have an obligation to the play the heck out of the ones you're holding." Do you agree?

5. Is it okay to quit on a dream? Is it possible to have multiple things that can bring us happiness, meaning and fulfillment?

6. Romans 12:4-5 says, "Be honest in your evaluation of yourselves, measuring yourselves by the faith God has given us." What is the best way to get an honest evaluation of our opportunities and barriers?

7. In what ways do you diminish your God-given gifts and abilities? Do you ever use the "I could never do that" excuse? Why is it so easy to dismiss what we're actually good at?

GROUP ACTIVITY

Share a strength, gift or special character trait that you have recognized in one of the group members. Take turns doing this.

I'VE KNOWN A LOT OF TALENTED, WONDERFUL PEOPLE WHO SHY AWAY FROM USING THEIR GOD-GIVEN GIFTS IN MORE PUBLIC WAYS BECAUSE OF THIS PHRASE "I COULD NEVER DO THAT!" AND AT FIRST IT SOUNDS SO HUMBLE. "I COULD NEVER MAKE A DIFFERENCE LIKE THOSE SUPER-TALENTED PEOPLE DO." AND THEN WE JUST KINDA LAUGH IT OFF. BUT THERE'S NOTHING HUMBLE OR THAT FUNNY ABOUT DIMINISHING THE GIFT THAT GOD HAS GIVEN YOU.

Excerpt from Session Three of the Wonderlife Videos

JUMP IN

———

LET'S TRY SOME STUFF
THIS WEEK

HONOR SOMEONE ONLINE

One of the most sacred things we can do as human beings is to recognize and find the good in others. So this week post a picture of someone on your social media platforms and talk about your favorite qualities of that person. Share how they have impacted your life or simply how you love their smile. It doesn't have to be long, just make sure to do it. It will mean a lot for the both of you. Use the hashtag #mywonderlife.

PICK YOUR BOARD MEMBERS

There is an old proverb that says, "If you want to go fast, go alone. If you want to go far, go with others." This week pick a friend, family member or someone that you trust and ask them to be a part of your personal board of directors. Give them access to your dreams, struggles and changes that you wish to make in your life. Creating accountability and interdependence will help set up your story for success.

Share online. Use the hashtag:

#MYWONDERLIFE

WRITE DOWN THINGS YOU
DON'T WANT TO FORGET HERE.

DRAW THINGS HERE.

I AM FULLY PRESENT IN MY LIFE

I AM FULLY ENGAGED AND PARTICIPATE IN GOD'S
BIG AND SMALL MIRACLES IN MY LIFE.

WE ALL HAVE
TWO LIVES.
THE SECOND
ONE STARTS WHEN
WE REALIZE
WE ONLY
HAVE
ONE.

-Tom Hiddleston

Let's talk for a minute about alarm clocks and how much we all hate them.

If you're one of those people who leap out of bed the minute the sun comes up—I'm happy for you. Really, I am. Because people like us need people like you to make us coffee! (Btw, that's a joke.)

I do not leap up when the alarm goes off. I groan. I sigh. I reject reality. And almost without thinking, my hand rises up out of those warm, snuggly sheets into the cold, heartless air and hits that most glorious of all inventions: the snooze button.

Whack-bam-thump! Zzzz.

Eight more minutes of sleepy-time bliss. Eight more minutes of not dealing with life. One little touch and all my problems, my challenges, my disappointments, my fears melt away into Sleepytown. The snooze button is a beautiful creation. And apparently I'm not the only one who thinks so.

Research shows the average person hits the snooze button two or three times before waking up. I even know some people who purposely set their alarm thirty minutes early just so they can hit it a bunch of times. But as with all delay tactics, you eventually have to pay the piper. You actually have to get up to wake up. The snoozing has to stop.

I've noticed a lot of people seem to hit the snooze bar on their life too. People feel the pull of a dream or the nudging of God to try something new, and *bam*—they hit snooze. Maybe they're out with a friend or spouse and the conversation starts to go beyond surface-level stuff and into things that really matter, and *bam*—they hit snooze. Or they feel the call to forgive, or be thankful, or do a small kind act like pray for someone and *bam*—they hit the button that sends those thoughts and feelings back to dreamland.

God tries to wake us, but we want to stay asleep. Because it's cold out there. It's demanding and disappointing. Life is risky and hurts sometimes. In a word—it's uncertain. We prefer the guarantee that doing nothing brings.

Did you know that uncertainty is just about the most avoided human emotion there is? People hate uncertainty. It can mean embarrassment, rejection and failure, so our hearts often prefer predictable pain to uncertain gain.

Researchers at Maastricht University in the Netherlands gave people a series of twenty electric shocks. One group got an intense shock every time—but they were told about the shock in advance. Another group received only three intense shocks and then the rest were mild, little zaps. But the little-zaps group didn't know when the big shock was coming.

So can you guess which group was more stressed out? The ones who got the milder shocks, because they never knew if a bad one was coming next! They sweat more. Their hearts raced. The uncertainty made them miserable even though they went through far less pain.

I think this is why Jesus told us to expect difficulties. He said, "Following me is a shocking experience. You will fail. You will get your heart broken. You will get in over your head. There might be three to four big zaps, but the rest will be just little shocks." Expecting it helps us deal with it all the better. We begin to risk more and fear less. We start to be fully present and meet God in every electric moment rather than trying to avoid the pain.

Don't bail out of life just because you don't know what might happen. Don't close off your heart to hope because you might get hurt. Don't numb out your feelings with drugs, Facebook binging or retail therapy shopping sprees rather than dealing with your feelings. That's escapism. It's a way to be absent when you are called to be present.

All of us have routines and things we do automatically. But here's a question for you: do you serve your routine or does it serve you? If your patterns of behavior keep you from connecting with

God, enjoying the now and being who you were made to be, then your routine is undermining your *wonderlife*.

If we want to be fully engaged in life, then here's a phrase we all need to take to heart: *bring the dream into the routine*. Bring a little bit of your someday goals into today's schedule. Get those habits working for you, not against you. If you want to enjoy life more, enjoy this moment He's given you. If you want to feel more loved, share more love. If you want your life to have more significance, do something small to make another person feel like they matter. And start today.

Ecclesiastes 11:4 (NLT) says, "Farmers who wait for perfect weather never plant. If they watch every cloud, they never harvest." So take a step today. And tomorrow. And the next day too. Put your dream into your routine.

I tell people all the time that if you want to see where you will be in five or ten years, just look at what you did today. Our lives are created in the small moments and choices of today. A big, God-sized life consists of a lot of little acts. Greatness is often overlooked because it's too tiny to see sometimes. It looks mundane and routine.

One of the mistakes I made in my life was that I used to have all my attention focused on living in the future. The present moments were just an afterthought and a mild nuisance to getting to where

I really wanted to go. It was always about next week, next year or the finish line. I rushed to build, create and conquer. Most of this was driven by my ego and fears of not being enough. It was a mistake and I missed the joy that today would bring.

I have found that there are two types of people who fail to fully grasp the power of the present. These individuals tend to be "hyper-past" or "hyper-future" focused. Both groups miss out on the wonder of the right-here, right-now life. Let me explain.

The hyper-past group are made up of "victims" who are defined by their hurt and the "romantics" who are stuck in their glory days. Victims are focused on blaming the world and live in the pain of the past. Romantics are stuck in the good-ole days and long for a time when life was easier and more rewarding.

The hyper-future focused group is made up of "planners" and "after-lifers." The planners miss out on today because their main focus is on building their giant nest egg. They put their life on hold until retirement. After-lifers are super-religious people who have no interest in this world and only wait around for heaven. Nothing on this planet really matters. They just punch the clock and count the days until they get their halos and angel wings.

Victims, romantics, planners and after-lifers fail to appreciate the incredible gift it is to be in this moment of time and to make the most of it. Their hearts and minds are someplace else. They don't see how God wants to use them right now in big and small ways.

Jesus describes a scene at the end of time where, upon his return as King, He divides the whole population of the world into two groups. The people on his right are praised and rewarded, while the people on his left are dismissed as worthless. Both groups are shocked and confused by how the King evaluates their lives. It all comes down to the smallest acts of love to the most overlooked people. Jesus says in Matthew 25:

I was hungry and you fed me, I was thirsty and you gave me a drink, I was homeless and you gave me a room, I was shivering and you gave me clothes, I was sick and you stopped to visit, I was in prison and you came to me.

I'm telling the solemn truth: Whenever you did one of these things to someone overlooked or ignored, that was me—you did it to me.

Greatness is not always big; sometimes it's tiny. You don't need to save the world, you just need to wake up and be fully present for life. Care for people only you can see. Give the gifts only you can give. Spread the joy you were made to share.

Looking back, you and I will probably be surprised at what our greatest acts really were. And shocked at how something so simple could matter so much.

"LIFE'S NO
PIECE OF CAKE,
MIND YOU,
BUT THE
RECIPE'S MY
OWN TO
FOOL WITH."

———

-Haruki Murakami

EXPLORE

EXERCISES TO HELP YOU
EXPLORE YOUR STORY

AND THE DAY
CAME WHEN THE
RISK TO REMAIN TIGHT
IN A BUD WAS MORE
PAINFUL THAN THE
RISK IT TOOK TO
BLOSSOM.

- Anaïs Nin

Theodore Roosevelt once said, "The best thing you can do is the right thing. The next best thing is the wrong thing and the worst thing is nothing." Use these two pages to start planning the next "right things" to your goal. Think about where you want to finish and then write out the steps as best as you can to getting there.

MY FIRST STEP IS...

TAKE A REST STOP. BUILD IN A TIME TO REPLENISH.

WHAT DOES
YOUR FINISH LINE
LOOK LIKE?

PARIS

NEW YORK

LONDON

DUBAI

**WHAT DESTINATIONS
WOULD YOU LOVE
TO EXPLORE?**

**CIRCLE THE CITY OR DESCRIBE
A PLACE THAT YOU WOULD
LOVE TO VISIT SOMEDAY.**

EXPLAIN WHY.

WONDERLIFE
BREAKOUT
NUGGET

THE POWER OF NOW

Now is a powerful moment. Think about it: You can
only enjoy things now. You can only love people now.
You can only live in this moment where the needle of
your life touches the spinning vinyl of eternity. Now is
where life's music is.

But sometimes we get sick of now because it's also
where the stress is. Now is where we feel pain, despair
and doubt. And when we do, we are tempted to do one
of two things: live in the past or live in the future.

If you find yourself wishing for the good old days and
longing for things to go back to how they used to be
you are no longer living, but reminiscing. Your past
should inform how you live and love today.

If you are a chronic worrier-dreamer-planner or just
someone who is positive that tomorrow will be better
and brighter than dumpy old today—you are no longer
living, but waiting. If you only live in the future, you
are losing today.

In what small ways in each day can you embrace
the power of now? List a few on this page.

Is your light...

Bright?

Dimming?

Out?

Piercing?

Flickering?

Beaming?

**YOU'RE HERE TO BE LIGHT, BRINGING OUT
THE GOD-COLORS IN THE WORLD.**
-Matthew 5:14, MSG

LITTLE MIRACLES

Check all that you
have experienced:

◯ MY BODY
WORKS

◯ WAKING UP
EACH MORNING

◯ HAVING
FRIENDS

◯ HAVING CLEAN
WATER TO DRINK

◯ LAUGHTER AND
SMILES

◯ THE ABILITY
TO DREAM

◯ SUNSETS AND
SUNRISES

◯ THE SMELL
OF BACON

◯ MUSIC AND
SONGS

◯ BREATHING

◯ RANDOM ACTS
OF KINDNESS

◯ SPRINGTIME

LIST OTHER AWESOME LITTLE MIRACLES
YOU HAVE EXPERIENCED IN YOUR LIFE:

. . . .

BIG MIRACLES

Check all that you have experienced:

- ○ BIRTH OF A CHILD
- ○ BEING LOVED UNCONDITIONALLY
- ○ GOD LOVING ME AS I AM
- ○ OVERCOMING ADDICTION
- ○ ALMOST DYING BUT NOW ALIVE
- ○ SURVIVING A HEALTH SCARE
- ○ GETTING A JOB I WANTED
- ○ HAVING A BEST FRIEND
- ○ GETTING THROUGH A TOUGH SEASON
- ○ ABILITY TO CHANGE
- ○ GRADUATING
- ○ GOD IS FOR ME

LIST OTHER AWESOME BIG MIRACLES YOU HAVE EXPERIENCED IN YOUR LIFE:

. . . .

FINALLY, BE STRONG IN THE LORD AND IN HIS MIGHTY POWER.
-Ephesians 6:10

EXPLORE YOUR COMFORT ZONES

Write a few of the big dreams, hopes and
plans that you have for your life.
Organize them into each zone.

"I'M KINDA
SCARED"
ZONE!

"I'M WILLING
TO GIVE IT A
TRY" ZONE!

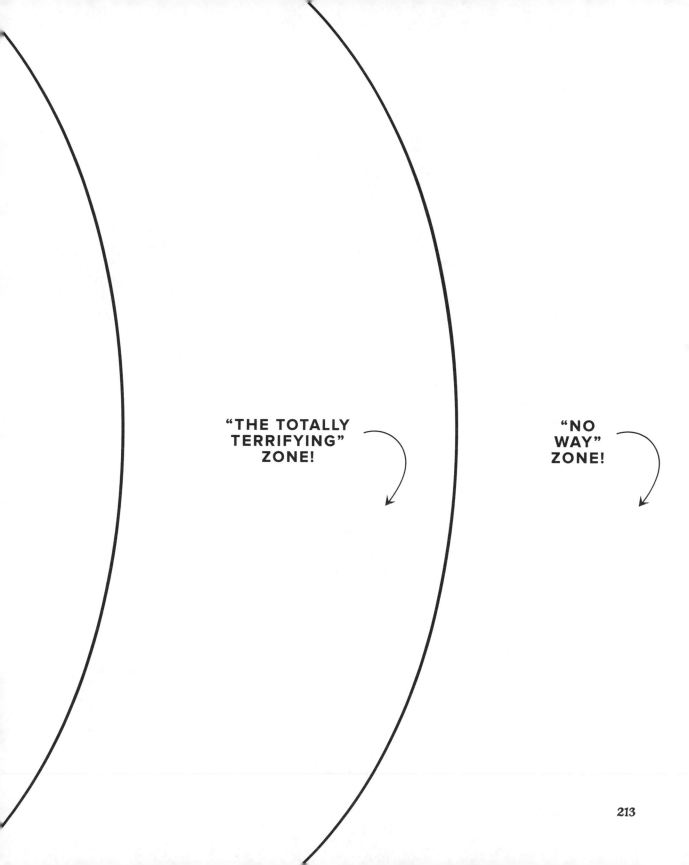

"THE TOTALLY TERRIFYING" ZONE!

"NO WAY" ZONE!

LITTLE ACTS OF LOVE

Living the *wonderlife* is about embracing the healing power of a small gesture. What small acts of love can you do right now?

INVITE SOMEONE TO LUNCH

PICK UP SHUT-INS FOR CHURCH

WRITE A ONE-LINE NOTE OF ENCOURAGEMENT

TREAT EVERYONE LIKE BEYONCE ON HER BIRTHDAY

MAKE COOKIES FOR CO-WORKERS

GIVE A HUG OR A HIGH FIVE

INTRODUCE YOURSELF TO A NEIGHBOR

OTHER THINGS YOU CAN DO

LET SOMEONE SCORE AN EASY BASKET ON YOU

**LET SOMEONE
BORROW ONE OF
YOUR BOOKS**

**CELEBRATE A FRIEND'S
BIRTHDAY EARLY**

**WRITE A SUPER NICE
COMMENT ON A
FRIEND'S POST**

**DON'T LET PEOPLE
LOSE HOPE**

**COMPLIMENT
YOUR SPOUSE**

**ASK A FRIEND TO
SHARE THEIR STORY**

**LISTEN REALLY
WELL TO OTHERS**

**PRAY FOR
SOMEONE'S
FAMILY AND KIDS**

**WHAT DO YOU THINK IS THE GREATEST ACT
OF LOVE THAT SOMEONE CAN DO FOR ANOTHER?**

. . . .

. . . .

NOW FAITH IS BEING SURE OF
WHAT WE HOPE FOR AND CERTAIN
OF WHAT WE DO NOT SEE.
-Hebrews 11:1

WONDERLIFE
BREAKOUT
NUGGET

THE SECRET OF _____

Sometimes we think, *Okay, once my schedule calms down, or I feel better or the house isn't a mess then I'll* _____. Or we say, "Once I get the training I need, or figure myself out, or get clarity from God, then I'll _____."

But here's the little secret about _____. You will never have clarity, never feel prepared and never have time until you actually start doing _____. You don't need to read a book, pray or get counsel before you start doing _____. You need to do all those things while you are doing _____.

The power comes along the way. The clarity comes along the way. The problems are solved along the way. So stop waiting. Find a need. Meet a need. Embrace today's work. God can fill in all the other blanks, but not until you fill that first one. You do the natural so God can do the supernatural. That is the secret of _____.

What _____ do you need to fill in today?

GROUP UP

MEET WITH YOUR FRIENDS AND TALK
ABOUT WHAT YOU'RE LEARNING

GROUP DISCUSSION QUESTIONS
"I AM FULLY PRESENT IN MY LIFE."

(Approximately 1 hour 15 minutes)

"If I go up to the heavens, you are there; if I make my
bed in the depths, you are there."
- Psalm 139:8, NIV

1. Wow! This is our last week of *Wonderlife*. Take some time to discuss what you've discovered about who you are and why you're here. What has been your favorite part? What surprised you? What challenged you? How have you been impacted by the people in this group?

2. In the workbook, Mike talked about how we love to hit the "snooze button" on our life. Why is this so easy to do? What does being "all in" with our life look like? Feel like? Sound like?

**NOW PLAY THE *WONDERLIFE* DVD OR STREAM THE GROUP
VIDEO AT SECONDCHANCE.ORG/VIDEO.**

3. What are some of the problems that come with us not fully showing up for our life? How do we lose out? How do others lose out too?

4. The apostle Paul says that the kingdom of God is at hand and graspable. What does that mean to you? How should that impact how we live and what we do?

5. Do you struggle with seeing the tiny miracles God is doing in your typical day? What is blocking your view? How could you increase the likelihood of not missing those little, sacred moments? How can you bring your dream into the routine?

6. What is the biggest distraction that keeps you from embracing all that God has for you? How could you nurture the now?

GROUP ACTIVITY

Plan a group get-together in the next couple weeks. Put together a dinner barbecue or grab brunch on a Sunday. Celebrate!

LISTEN, YOUR PURPOSE, YOUR DESTINY
IS WAITING JUST OUTSIDE. THE
WINDOW IS OPEN. THE SKY AWAITS.
THE KINGDOM OF GOD IS AT HAND.
AND HE LOOKS AT YOU AND ME AND
SAYS, "HEY, GUYS, YOU READY? YOU
READY TO FLY? YOU READY TO LOVE?
YOU READY TO HAVE SOME FUN? YOU
READY TO LIVE THE *WONDERLIFE*?
ALL RIGHT, THEN LET'S GO!"

Excerpt from Session Four of
the Wonderlife Videos

JUMP IN

LET'S TRY SOME STUFF
THIS WEEK

EXPAND THE COMFORT ZONE

Pick a day this week when you will operate against your normal routine. Try to identify an unhelpful habit or routine and do the opposite of what you normally do. If you feel like you're stuck in a rut, you probably are. The only way to break free from a rut is to do things differently.

WAKING UP

On a piece of paper, write a list of three things that you want to accomplish this month. Maybe you want to learn a skill. Perhaps you have a goal to read a certain number of books. Maybe you want to start developing a new business idea. Perhaps you want to adopt a cat from the animal shelter. Each night, put the list under your pillow. Each morning, pull it out, but only if you're willing to work on it. If you want to just hit the snooze on life, leave the list under your pillow until you're ready.

Share online. Use the hashtag:
#MYWONDERLIFE

WRITE DOWN THINGS YOU
DON'T WANT TO FORGET.

DRAW THINGS HERE.

A FINAL WORD

And now, my friends, I leave you with one of my favorite poems by Saint Teresa of Avila that captures my prayer for your *wonderlife* with God.

JUST THESE TWO WORDS HE SPOKE
CHANGED MY LIFE, "ENJOY ME."

WHAT A BURDEN I THOUGHT I WAS
TO CARRY—A CRUCIFIX, AS DID HE.

LOVE ONCE SAID TO ME, "I KNOW A SONG,
WOULD YOU LIKE TO HEAR IT?"

AND LAUGHTER CAME FROM EVERY BRICK
IN THE STREET AND EVERY PORE IN THE SKY.

AFTER A NIGHT OF PRAYER, HE CHANGED
MY LIFE WHEN HE SANG, "ENJOY ME."

-Saint Teresa of Avila

Mike Foster is an author, speaker and lover of imperfectionists. He is the founder of People of the Second Chance and the best-selling author of *Freeway: A Not-So-Perfect Guide to Freedom*. He lives in San Diego with his family and his fluffy dog.

You can contact him at SecondChance.org or at his website, MikeFoster.tv.

Twitter: @MikeFoster
Instagram: MikeFoster2000
Hashtag: #mywonderlife

PEOPLE OF THE
SECOND
CHANCE

People of the Second Chance is a nonprofit organization guided by this lofty ideal: that every person on earth deserves a second chance. We believe that taking ownership of the broken things within us and around us is the key to redeeming the future.

www.SecondChance.org
Contact@SecondChance.org

THANK YOU

I want to first thank you for going through this workbook. It is such an honor for me to have our lives be connected through this experience.

I want to especially thank Scott Pace and the amazing People of the Second Chance Team. Your fingerprints and pixie dust are all over this project. Also, Justin Jackson for adding your brilliance, insights and words. Your contribution was immense and profound. Ashton Owens for your design and creativity. Jud Wilhite for your constant encouragement and best-friendship. Bill Townsend for helping me believe in myself again and helping me discover my own wonderlife. Of course, Mom and Dad and Kristen for everything. Kevin and Robin Small for helping me figure out these concepts over Mexican food. The Michalski family. Shannon Sedgwick-Davis. Brian Johnson. Daley Hake. Ryan O'Neal. Jon Acuff. Bill Hybels, Anne Rand, Jorie Johnson and Willow Creek Church for helping bring this project to life and for believing in it enough to give it to seventy thousand inmates in Illinois. Wow! My Vegas family at Central Christian Church and all my fellow imperfectionists around the globe. I love you!

And most of all, Jennifer, Jackson and Taylor Foster for letting me experience my own wonderlife with you.

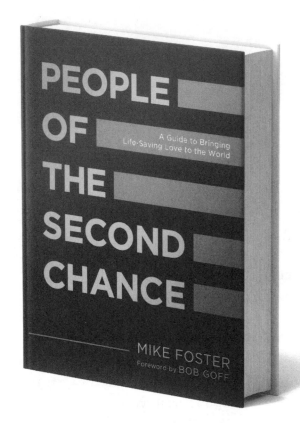

CALLING ALL IMPERFECTIONISTS AND HOPESTERS

People of the Second Chance: A Guide To Bringing Life-Saving Love To The World is the highly anticipated new book from Mike Foster that will stir a generation of imperfectionists to live as the beloved and throw prodigal parties. With the fierceness of a lion and the down-to-earth style of Mr. Rogers, this book will feel like an arousing pep-talk and a big warm hug.

Available wherever books are sold.

A NOT-SO-PERFECT GUIDE TO FREEDOM

Freeway is a small-group curriculum and weekend experience created by Mike Foster to help people experience real freedom in their lives. Over 100,000 people and 500 churches have gone through this innovative six-step process, which was voted a top-five church campaign by Rick Warren's *Pastors.com*.

Learn more about *Freeway* and
Rescue Lab & Academy at:
SECONDCHANCE.ORG

rescue lab

Rescue Lab is a two-day, intensive workshop designed to teach you the skills and strategies to help coach and counsel people. With our exclusive content and interactive learning format, *Rescue Lab* will unleash your passion to impact people's lives forever. The *Rescue Lab* workshop is facilitated by Mike Foster.

rescue
A C A D E M Y

Rescue Academy is a seven-part online course to help transform you from an advice-giver to a life-giver. In this online academy you will learn how to positively impact friends, family and the people that you work with and develop your passion for helping people transform their lives.

NOTES

The house exercise in Lifemark #1 was inspired by my friend
Dave Gibbons.

The personal board of directors concept came from a Harvard
Business Review article I read by Priscilla Claman.

Lewis B. Smedes inspired the hyper-future and hyper-past focus
concept discussed in Lifemark #4.

The phrase "only broken things can make broken things
beautiful again" came from a wonderful conversation with my
friend Jason Russell.

Dallas Willard and Richard Rohr have profoundly shaped many of
the ideas in this workbook and in my life. I'm grateful for these
two men.

Thanks to Ksyu Denisenko for the beautiful animal drawings.

Thank you to all those who allowed me to include your quotes
throughout this book. I'm inspired by your words.

Psalm 139 is the basis for this concept and the four lifemarks
discussed in *Wonderlife*.

The *Wonderlife* videos were filmed by Daley Hake and the
awesome soundtrack is by Sleeping At Last.

WRITE DOWN THINGS YOU
DON'T WANT TO FORGET.

&

www.SecondChance.org